In Cresskill, New Jersey, all cats must wear three bells to warn birds of their whereabouts.

Why do ducks waddle? Ducks waddle because their legs are situated way in back of their bodies.

It's against the law to take a French poodle to an opera house in Chicago.

How do lions spend most of their time?
Eating and sleeping.

Which animal looks most like a masked bandit? The raccoon.

In Sterling, Colorado, it is unlawful to allow a pet cat to run loose without a taillight.

The town of Butler, Indiana, officially adopted an orphaned fawn in 1971 and allowed it to roam freely through the town.

Why are dogs often called Fido? "Fido" is the Latin word for "faithful," a quality almost every dog possesses.

How do horses communicate with one another? A variety of sounds such as whinnies and squeals all have special meaning to other horses.

What is a bear's favorite treat? Honey.

Can animals see in color? Most cannot, except for monkeys and apes.

In Knoxville, Tennessee, the law says you must call a police officer if a tiger or lion brushes against you in the street.